Taking care of Myself

	Page	CD track Vocal	backing
INTRODUCTION	3	–	
LYRICS & TEACHER'S NOTES	4	–	
THE SONGS			
All By Myself*	16	1	13
Blow Your Nose	18	2	14
What Goes In Your Socks Sam?*	20	3	15
When Mummy Says "Get Ready"*	22	4	16
Splish, Splash!*	25	5	17
Careful How You Cross	28	6	18
Can You Help Me Please?*	30	7	19
Too Many Toffees*	32	8	20
Healthy Heart	34	9	21
Eat Nicely	36	10	22
Tidy Up!*	39	11	23
What Good Strong Teeth	42	12	24

* Especially suitable for early years

Introduction

The  series of books is a brand new collection of topic-based songbooks. Each includes twelve easy-to-learn and catchy songs by some of Britain's most popular children's songwriters. The accompanying CD features all songs sung by children along with professionally produced backing tracks.

Developed specifically for pre-school and reception aged children, we feel that the music and topics covered will also be particularly appropriate for use with children up to the age of around seven. The songs can be used to supplement the 'creative' requirements of the foundation stage, as well as contributing to many other areas of the curriculum. Each lyric page contains helpful teacher's notes to expand and develop the subject content of the songs.

In addition to the teaching ideas given with each song, we suggest adding some simple percussion using instruments available in the classroom, and perhaps some homemade ones. It's important that children relate to music as something that they can become actively involved with and enjoy. Using percussion and easy clapping rhythms gives everyone a chance to really join in.

All By Myself

Words and Music by Niki Davies
CCLI Song No. 4373711

1. I can put my jumper on,
   I can put my jumper on,
   Just watch me, then you'll see,
   Right arm, left arm,
   All by myself.

2. I can wash behind my ears,
   I can wash behind my ears,
   Just watch me, then you'll see,
   Right ear, left ear,
   All by myself.

3. I can tie my laces up,
   I can tie my laces up,
   Just watch me, then you'll see,
   Right shoe, left shoe,
   All by myself.

4. I can tap my feet in time,
   I can tap my feet in time,
   Just watch me, then you'll see,
   Right, left, right, left,
   All by myself.

As well as being a great song for beginning to learn left and right, this is a wonderful action song. Get the children to mime the different actions as they sing through the verses. Perhaps they can think of their own verses involving activities that use left and right.

Blow Your Nose

Words and Music by Ann Beresford
CCLI Song No. 4373728

When your nose is feeling runny,
Please don't sniff.
Though you think it's very funny
Please don't sniff!
Take a tissue, hold it flat,
Place it on your nose like that,
Blow a little, wipe it well,
Blow, blow, blow!

Repeat song

Blowing your nose is something that a lot of children find hard to master.
This song is great for getting them started.

Talk about colds and how they make you feel. How does your nose feel
when you've got a cold? Does your body feel any different? What things
help you feel better when you're ill?

What Goes In Your Socks Sam?

Words and Music by Ali McClure
(Dedicated to Ivy)
CCLI Song No. 4373735

1. What goes in your socks Sam?
   What goes in your socks?
   What goes in your socks Sam?
   What goes in your socks?
   Is it your nose?
   Is it your toes?

2. What goes in your shoes Sam? …
   Is it a sweet?
   Is it your feet?

3. What goes in your trousers Sam? …
   Is it some eggs?
   Is it your legs?

4. What goes in your glove Sam? …
   Is it some sand?
   Is it your hand?

5. What goes in your sleeve Sam? …
   Is it a farm?
   Is it your arm?

6. What goes in your hat Sam? …
   Is it a bed?
   Is it your head?

Learning to get dressed is an important part of physical and emotional development – choosing what we'd like to wear that day, being able to co-ordinate our heads, arms and legs into the right 'holes', and beginning to take responsibility for ourselves.

Talk to the children about words that rhyme. They will have a lot of fun thinking of more rhyming words to make up new verses for this song.

When Mummy Says "Get Ready"

Words and Music by Ann Beresford

CCLI Song No. 4373742

When Mummy says "Get ready",
Well what should you say?
"OK Mummy, OK."
When Mummy says "Get ready",
Well what should you do?
Wash your face and run to the loo!

Brush your teeth, *(sh, sh, sh, sh)*
And comb your hair (*"Don't you look smart!"*),
Put on your coat, *(uh, uh, uh, uh)*
And wave goodbye. *(kiss, kiss, kiss, kiss)*
When Mummy says "Get ready",
Well what should you say?
"OK Mummy, OK."

Repeat whole song

Discuss why it is important to be ready on time.

Ask the children to discuss what routines they have to follow in their own homes. Ask the children to predict what will happen if they do not follow their routines.

Give each child a piece of paper divided into four, with a picture of an 'empty' mummy's face at the bottom. In the four quarters, ask the children to draw the most important ways to help mummy in the morning. Then, the children could draw in a happy mummy or a sad mummy, depending on whether everyone had helped to 'get ready' that day.

Splish, Splash!

Words and Music by Ann Beresford

CCLI Song No. 4373759

Splish splash, splish splash,
In the bath.
Splish splash, splish splash,
In the bath.
Wiggle waggle, wiggle waggle,
Wiggle all your toes,
Be careful you don't get the bubbles up your nose!

1. You dip your *big toe* in the water,
   Make sure it's not too hot,
   You pour the bubbles in,
   And you swish it round a lot.
   You get your soap and flannel and your favourite toys,
   Scrub your grubby knees and make a lot of noise.

   CHORUS

2. You dip your *elbow* in the water,
   Make sure it's not too hot,
   You pour the bubbles in,
   And you swish it round a lot.
   You get your soap and flannel and your favourite toys,
   Wash behind your ears and make a lot of noise.

   CHORUS

3. You dip your *bottom* in the water,
   Make sure it's not too hot,
   You pour the bubbles in,
   And you swish it round a lot.
   You get your soap and flannel and your favourite toys,
   Wash yourself all over, make a lot of noise.

   CHORUS *(last line twice)*

Discuss why it's important to keep clean. Apart from bath time, when else do we need to make sure parts of our body are clean, for example, before we eat and after we've been to the toilet?

careful How You cross

Words and Music by Mark and Helen Johnson
CCLI Song No. 4373766

1. When the roads are full of traffic,
   Careful how you cross the road.
   When a friend is waving at you,
   Careful how you cross the road.

   Stop by the kerb,
   Hold someone's hand,
   Don't cross the road 'til you're told you can.
   Watch while you wait,
   Make sure it's safe,
   Think as you cross. Don't run!

2. When the streets are not so busy,
   Careful how you cross the road.
   When you're late and in a hurry,
   Careful how you cross the road.

   CHORUS

3. When the days are warm and sunny,
   Careful how you cross the road.
   When it's wet and when it's windy,
   Careful how you cross the road.

Can the children name some of the safest places to cross the road, eg pelican and zebra crossings? Talk about waiting for the traffic to stop and watching for the 'green man' before they begin to cross. Why is it important to walk not run on a crossing?

Perhaps the children could paint a picture of a busy road with some people waiting to cross over. See how many different types of vehicles they can include on the road.

Can You Help Me Please?

Words and Music by Sha Armstrong
CCLI Song No. 4373773

1. Sometimes things are hard to do,
   Tie your laces, tie your laces.
   Sometimes things are not so easy,
   Can you help me please,
   Can you help me please?

2. Sometimes things are hard to do,
   Put your coat on, put your coat on.
   Sometimes things are not so easy,
   Can you help me please,
   Can you help me please?

3. Sometimes things are hard to do,
   Paint a picture, paint a picture.
   Sometimes things are not so easy,
   Can you help me please,
   Can you help me please?

It's important that children know there are some things that we can't always do by ourselves, and on these occasions it's good to be able to ask for help.

Can the children think of other things that they need help to do and make up some more verses to the song?

Too Many Toffees

Words and Music by Niki Davies

CCLI Song No. 4373845

1. Don't let your teeth go rotten,
    Don't let your teeth fall out.
    Don't let your teeth go rotten,
    There are too many *toffees* about.
    Too many *toffees*, too many *toffees*,
    Too many *toffees* about!

2. Too many *cookies* …

3. Too many *lollies* …

4. Too many *cakes* …

5. Too many *sweets* …

This song talks about lots of the 'wrong' things to eat if we want to keep a healthy diet. How many 'healthy' foods can the children think of? Talk about how we can eat five portions of fruit and vegetables each day to help stay healthy, and the effect that good and bad food has on our bodies.

Cut some card into two life-size people shapes and attach these to the wall. Ask the children to find pictures of lots of different food from magazines and get them to cut these out. Sort the food into 'healthy' and 'unhealthy' and then get the children to stick all the healthy food onto one of the people, and the unhealthy food onto the other.

Healthy Heart

Words and Music by Margaret Carpenter
CCLI Song No. 4373852

1. *Running* is a way to keep a healthy heart,
   Even if you're little you can make a start.
   Feel your heart, is it pumping strong?
   Just what it needs to help the blood along.
   Running is a way to keep a healthy heart,
   Try it and you'll have a healthy heart!

2. *Jumping* is a way to keep a healthy heart,
   Even if you're little you can make a start.
   Feel your heart, is it pumping strong?
   Just what it needs to help the blood along.
   Jumping is a way to keep a healthy heart,
   Try it and you'll have a healthy heart!

3. *Skipping* is a way to keep a healthy heart,
   Even if you're little you can make a start.
   Feel your heart, is it pumping strong?
   Just what it needs to help the blood along.
   Skipping is a way to keep a healthy heart,
   Try it and you'll have a healthy heart!

4. *Dancing* is a way to keep a healthy heart,
   Even if you're little you can make a start.
   Feel your heart, is it pumping strong?
   Just what it needs to help the blood along.
   Dancing is a way to keep a healthy heart,
   Try it and you'll have a healthy heart!

Whilst singing the song, can the children do the exercise for each verse – eg run on the spot in the first verse, skip around the room in the third, and so on?

Before you begin singing, ask the children to put their hands over their hearts to see if they can feel it pumping. At the end of the song, do this again – can they feel their heart pumping harder now?

Eat Nicely

Words and Music by Alison Hedger
CCLI Song No. 4373869

1. Please don't chew with your mouth open wide,
    We don't want to see what's going on inside.
    Munching, crunching, churning, turning,
    A really disgusting sight! Right?

2. Please don't chew with your mouth open wide,
    We don't want to see what's going on inside.
    Slurping, burping, gnashing, splashing,
    Munching, crunching, churning, turning,
    A really disgusting sight! Right?

3. Please don't chew with your mouth open wide,
    We don't want to see what's going on inside.
    Licking, sticking, flicking, spitting,
    Slurping, burping, gnashing, splashing,
    Munching, crunching, churning, turning,
    A really disgusting sight!

    Spoken (mother's exasperated voice):
    For the last time, <u>please</u> eat with your mouth closed!

You should have some fun trying to get your tongue around some of these lyrics! It doesn't matter if the children get a bit tongue-tied.

Look around to find some things to help make the noises featured in the song, for example screwed up paper for 'crunching'; water for 'splashing'; running a pencil along a comb for 'burping' and so on. Various percussion instruments and the children's own voices will make some of the other noises.

Use these sounds to create a sound picture. Imagine that you are eating a large plate of food (the children can think of lots of 'noisy' food to eat). As each mouthful goes in, begin to build up the different sounds one by one, until there is far too much food being chewed around noisily in the mouth. Eventually, after lots of munching and crunching, the food is swallowed and the noise suddenly stops. If the children are feeling particularly cheeky, they could finish with a big burp!

Tidy Up!

Words and Music by Mark and Helen Johnson
CCLI Song No. 4373876

1. Once in a while,
   Every now and then,
   Places that were tidy become a mess again.
   Things on the floor,
   Things everywhere,
   Oh, what a muddle we're in!

   But we can …

   Tidy up! Tidy up!
   How many things can we put away?
   Pick them up, put them back,
   Come on everybody, let's be tidy today!

2. Once in a while,
   Every now and then,
   Places that were tidy become a mess again.
   Things on the floor,
   Things everywhere,
   Oh, what a muddle we're in!

   But we can …

   Tidy up! Tidy up!
   How many things can we put away?
   Pick them up, put them back,
   Come on everybody, let's be tidy today!

   Tidy up! Tidy up!
   How many things can we put away?
   Pick them up, put them back,
   Come on everybody, let's be tidy today!
   Come on everybody, let's be tidy today!

A great song to use at the end of 'free-play' time or the end of the day!

Try combining the tidying with some sorting games too – sort toys by colour; type; size; shape; materials and so on.

What Good Strong Teeth

Words and Music by Sha Armstrong
CCLI Song No. 4373883

1. Keep your toothbrush close at hand,
    Spread the toothpaste if you can,
    Brush your teeth both night and day,
    Then you'll hear the dentist say …

    "What good strong teeth, you've kept them clean,
    What good strong teeth, you clever thing,
    What good strong teeth, they're all just fine."
    Now the dentist is a friend of mine!

    "What good strong teeth, you've kept them clean,
    What good strong teeth, you clever thing,
    What good strong teeth, they're all just fine."
    Now the dentist is a friend of mine!

2. Help your teeth feel good as new,
    Just remember what to do,
    Brush your teeth both night and day,
    Then you'll hear the dentist say …

    CHORUS
    Friend of mine! Friend of mine!

Do any of the children know how many teeth they have? Talk about how and when we get our first set of teeth (milk teeth). Do any of the children have baby brothers or sisters? Have they got any teeth yet? How do the babies feel when their teeth are coming through?

Talk about what happens to our milk teeth and how when we lose them we grow another set of teeth. Discuss how we can help to keep our teeth healthy – by brushing thoroughly and regularly and by eating less sugary foods.

All By Myself

Words and Music by
Niki Davies

Bright & rhythmic (♩ = 175)

1. I can put my jump - er on,___
2. I can wash be - hind my ears,___
3. I can tie my lac - es up,___
4. I can tap my feet in time,___

I can put my jump - er on,___ just watch me,
I can wash be - hind my ears,___ just watch me,
I can tie my lac - es up,___ just watch me,
I can tap my feet in time,___ just watch me,

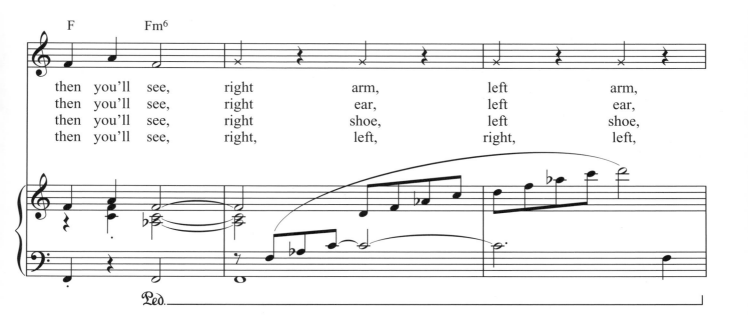

then you'll see, right arm, left arm,
then you'll see, right ear, left ear,
then you'll see, right shoe, left shoe,
then you'll see, right, left, right, left,

all by my - self!
all by my - self!
all by my - self!
all by my - self!

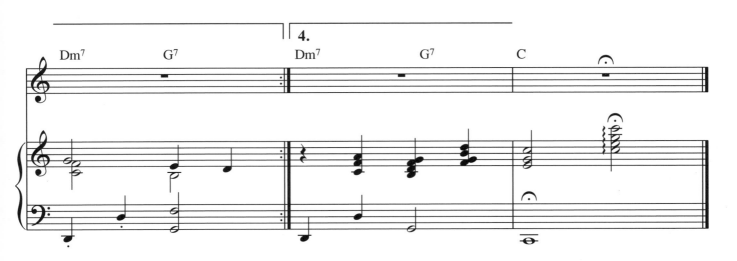

Blow Your Nose

Words and Music by
Ann Beresford

Light & bright (♩ = 170)

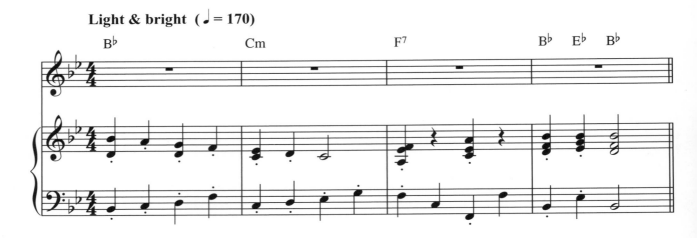

When your nose is feel-ing run-ny, please don't sniff.

Though you think it's ve-ry fun-ny, please don't sniff!

Take a tis - sue, hold it flat, place it on your nose like that,

blow a lit - tle, wipe it well, blow, blow, blow!

1.

2.

What Goes In Your Socks Sam?

Words and Music by
Ali McClure

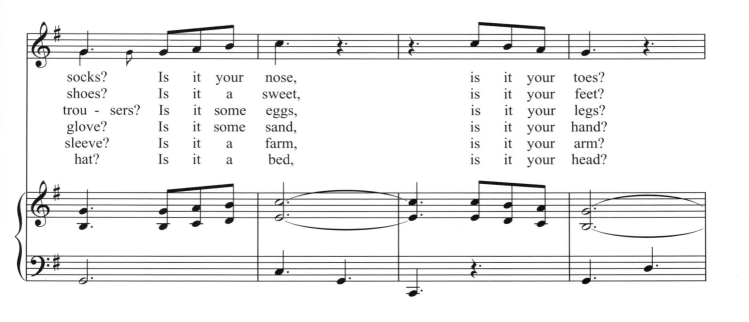

socks?   Is   it   your   nose,   is   it   your   toes?
shoes?   Is   it   a   sweet,   is   it   your   feet?
trou - sers?   Is   it   some   eggs,   is   it   your   legs?
glove?   Is   it   some   sand,   is   it   your   hand?
sleeve?   Is   it   a   farm,   is   it   your   arm?
hat?   Is   it   a   bed,   is   it   your   head?

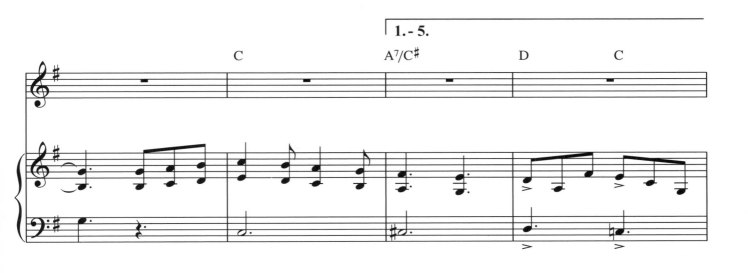

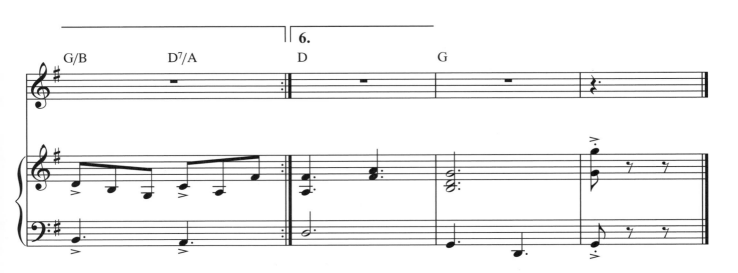

When Mummy Says "Get Ready"

Words and Music by
Ann Beresford

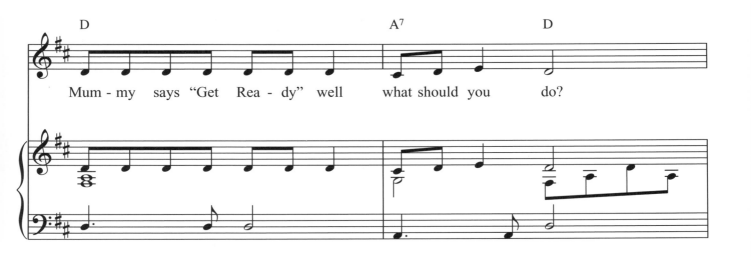

Mum-my says "Get Rea-dy" well what should you do?

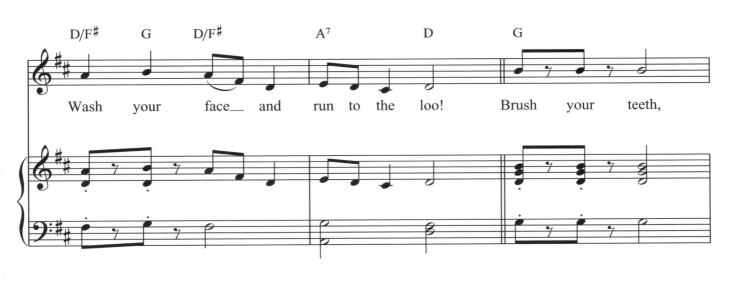

Wash your face__ and run to the loo! Brush your teeth,

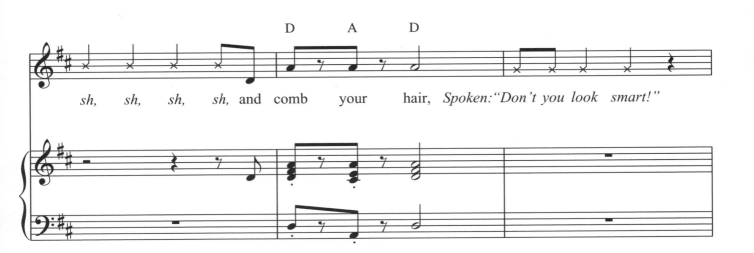

sh, sh, sh, sh, and comb your hair, *Spoken:"Don't you look smart!"*

23

put on your coat, *uh, uh, uh, uh,* and say good - bye.

(kiss or wave) When Mum-my says "Get Rea-dy" well what should you say?

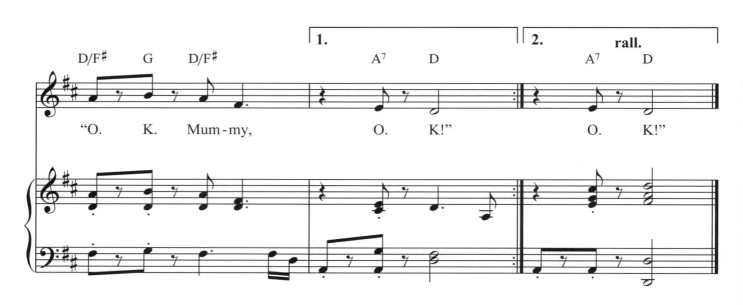

"O. K. Mum-my, O. K!" O. K!"

Splish, Splash!

Words and Music by
Ann Beresford

Medium tempo (♩ = 110)

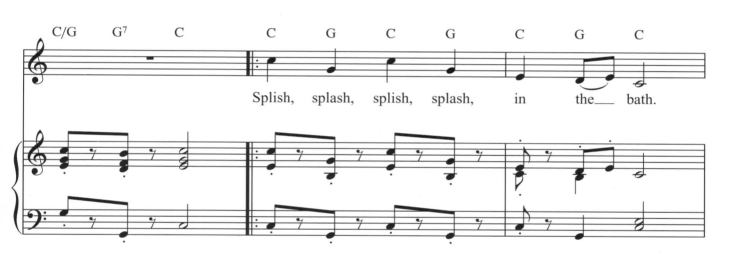

Splish, splash, splish, splash, in the___ bath.

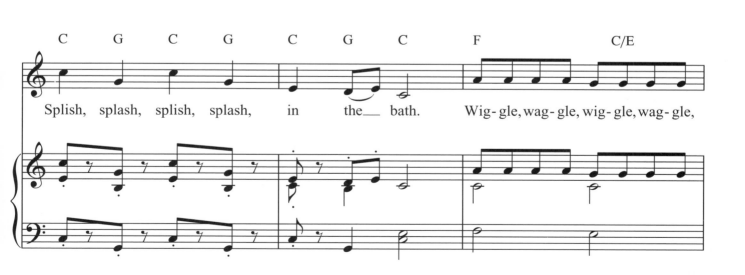

Splish, splash, splish, splash, in the___ bath. Wig-gle, wag-gle, wig-gle, wag-gle,

4th time to Coda ⊕

G⁷/D   C   Dm⁷   C/G   G⁷   C

wig-gle all your toes,   be   care-ful you don't get the bub-bles up   your   nose!

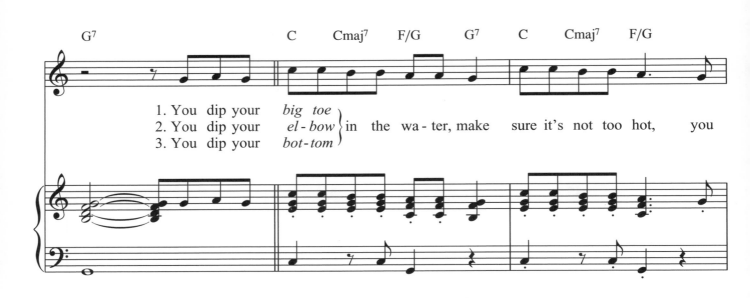

G⁷   C   Cmaj⁷   F/G   G⁷   C   Cmaj⁷   F/G

1. You dip your   *big toe*
2. You dip your   *el-bow* } in the wa-ter, make   sure it's not too hot,   you
3. You dip your   *bot-tom*

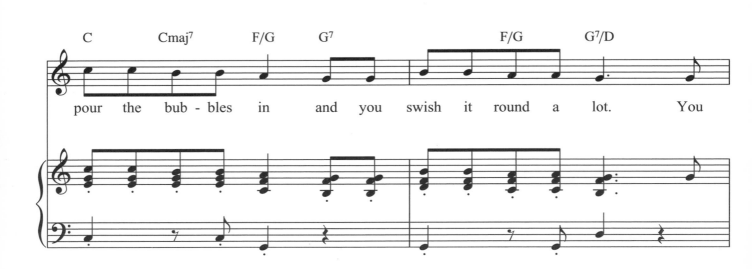

C   Cmaj⁷   F/G   G⁷   F/G   G⁷/D

pour the bub - bles in   and you swish it round a   lot.   You

Careful How You Cross

Words and Music by
Mark and Helen Johnson

cross the road.___
cross the road.___ Stop by the kerb, hold some-one's hand,

don't cross the road 'til you're told you can;___ watch while you wait,

make sure it's safe, think as you cross. Don't run!

2.
D. 𝄋 al Coda

run!

CODA

rall.

care - ful how you cross the road.

Can You Help Me Please?

Words and Music by
Sha Armstrong

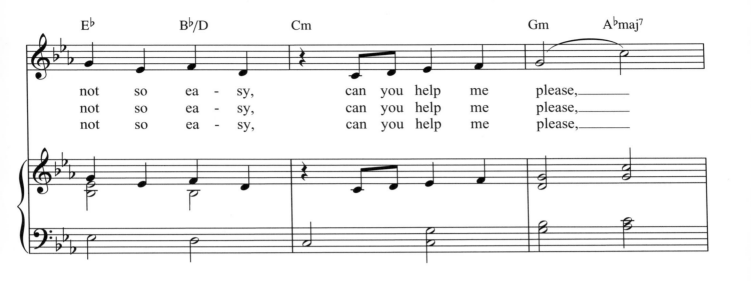

not so ea - sy, can you help me please,_____
not so ea - sy, can you help me please,_____
not so ea - sy, can you help me please,_____

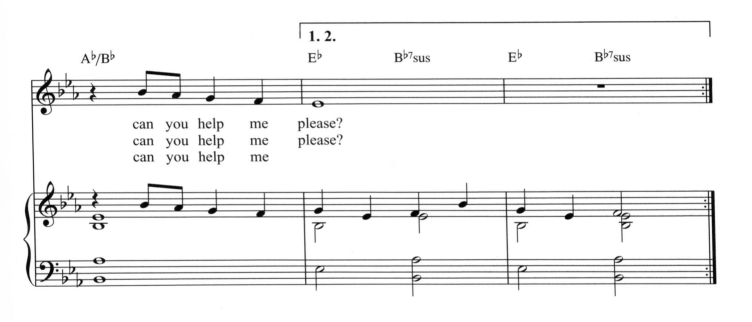

1. 2.

can you help me please?
can you help me please?
can you help me

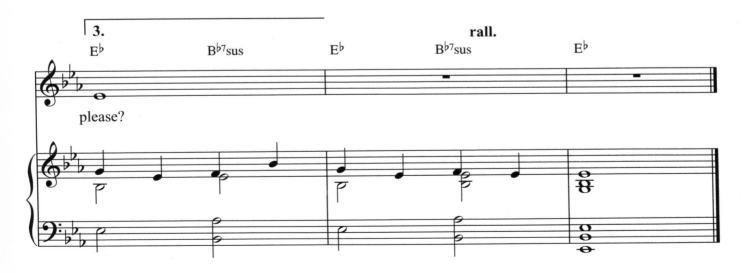

3.   **rall.**

please?

Too Many Toffees

Words and Music by
Niki Davies

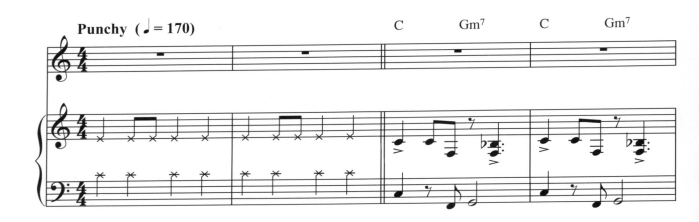

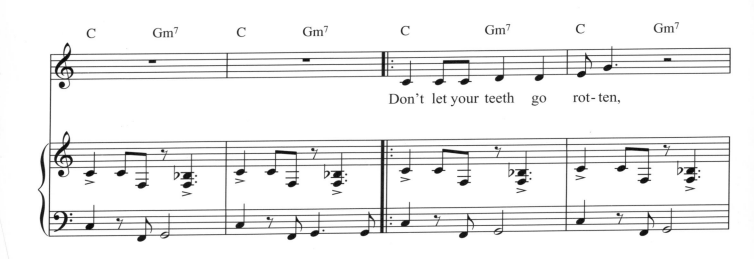

33

Healthy Heart

Words and Music by
Margaret Carpenter

Steady tempo (♩ = 120)

1. Run - ning
2. Jump - ing is a way to keep a heal - thy heart,
3. Skip - ping
4. Danc - ing

ev - en if you're lit - tle you can make a start. Feel your heart, is it

Eat Nicely

Words and Music by
Alison Hedger

1. Please don't chew with your mouth o - pen wide,
2. Please don't chew with your mouth o - pen wide,
3. Please don't chew with your mouth o - pen wide,

we don't want to see what's go - ing on in - side.
we don't want to see what's go - ing on in - side.
we don't want to see what's go - ing on in - side.

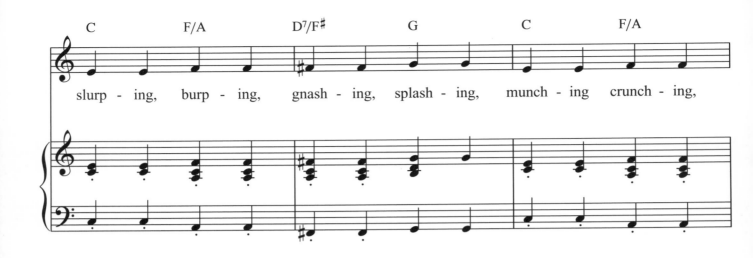

slurp - ing, burp - ing, gnash - ing, splash - ing, munch - ing crunch - ing,

churn - ing, turn - ing, a real - ly dis - gust - ing

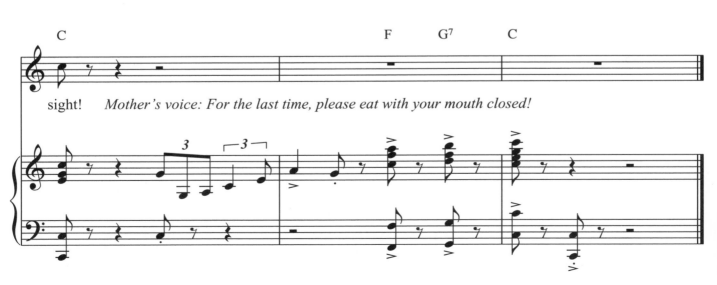

sight! *Mother's voice: For the last time, please eat with your mouth closed!*

Tidy Up!

Words and Music by
Mark and Helen Johnson

Once in a while, ev - ery now and then,

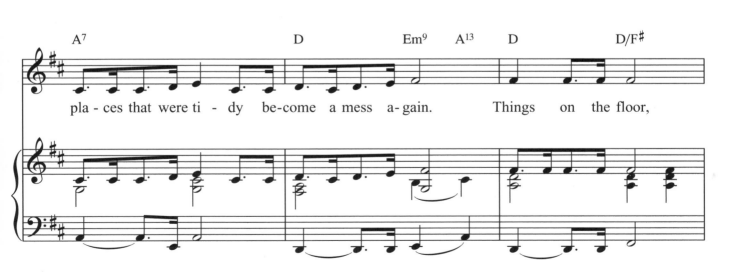

pla - ces that were ti - dy be - come a mess a - gain. Things on the floor,

things ev-ery-where, Oh, what a mud-dle we're in! But we can...

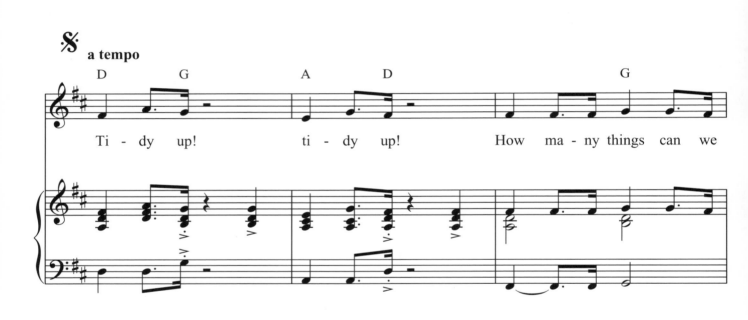

Ti - dy up! ti - dy up! How ma - ny things can we

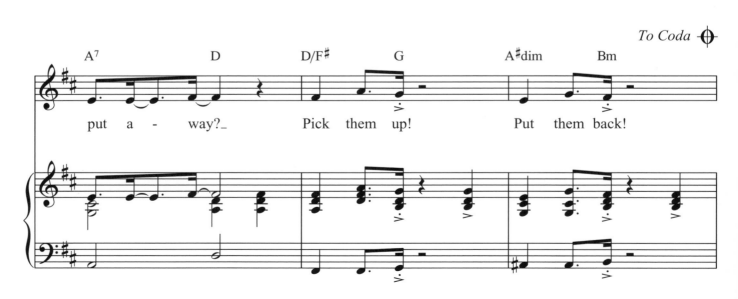

put a - way?_ Pick them up! Put them back!

40

What Good Strong Teeth!

Words and Music by
Sha Armstrong

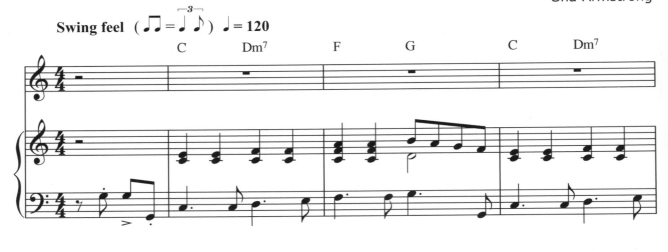

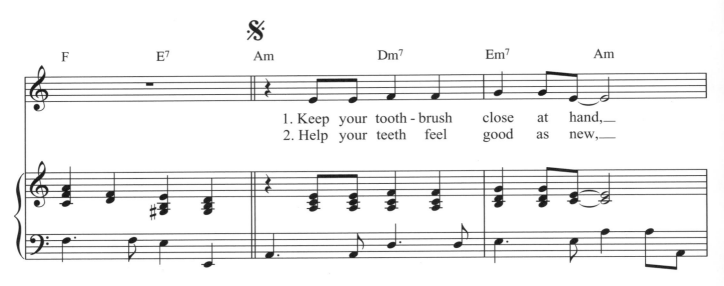

1. Keep your tooth-brush close at hand,
2. Help your teeth feel good as new,

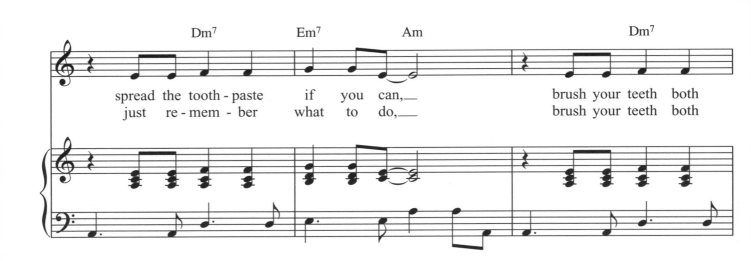

spread the tooth-paste if you can,___ brush your teeth both
just re-mem-ber what to do,___ brush your teeth both